D1361709

DEDICATED TO THE STARS AND THE STRIPES AND THE COLORS THAT BOND THEM TOGETHER

www.mascotbooks.com

Founders Force Thomas Jefferson: Truth Jotter and Free Speech

For more information, please contact:
Mascot Books
560 Herndon Parkway #120
Herndon, VA 20170
info@mascotbooks.com

Library of Congress Control Number: 2015903478

CPSIA Code: PRT0415A
ISBN-13: 978-1-63177-078-4

Printed in the United States…'Merica!

FOUNDERS FORCE

Thomas Jefferson

Truth Jotter and Free Speech

Written by
Kyle and Brandi McElhaney

Illustrated by
Michael Nozinich

THOMAS JEFFERSON, KNOWN AS TJ TO HIS FRIENDS, WAS DRAWING BUILDINGS AND READING BOOKS AT HIS HOUSE. ALL OF A SUDDEN, A KNOCK AT THE DOOR REVEALED A MESSENGER BOY.

THE BOY CLEARLY HAD BEEN RUNNING AS FAST AS HIS LEGS COULD TAKE HIM TO GET A MESSAGE TO TJ'S HOME, LOVINGLY NAMED MONTICELLO.

THE BOY WAS RIGHT. WHAT TJ SAW HORRIFIED HIM. THE EVIL KING WAS AT IT AGAIN! HE WAS NOT ONLY STEALING THE AMERICANS' HARD-EARNED MONEY, HE WAS ALSO THROWING *THEM* IN JAIL WHEN THEY SPOKE OUT AGAINST IT!

TJ KNEW SOMETHING HAD TO BE DONE. MEN MUST BE ABLE TO SPEAK THEIR MINDS WITHOUT FEAR THEY WILL BE JAILED.

AFTER MANY LONG DAYS AND NIGHTS OF WRITING, TJ WAS READY. HIS PERFECTLY-CRAFTED DOCUMENT WOULD ALLOW PEOPLE TO SPEAK FREELY AGAINST VILLAINS AND THIEVES. IT JUST NEEDED TO BE REVIEWED BEFORE HE SIGNED IT AND MADE IT PERMANENT.

His friends in the Virginia Congress loved it! This was just what they needed to put the King in his place and let people speak freely forever. They begged him to sign it and deliver a permanent blow.

TJ UNSHEATHED HIS MAGIC QUILL AND HELD IT HIGH ABOVE HIS HEAD.

THE CONGRESSMEN CHEERED, KNOWING WHAT WOULD HAPPEN NEXT.

At the very second TJ finished the last swoop in the last letter of his last name, with the power of the pen and the power of all that is right, he ensured this document would be a part of America forever.

THE KING HEARD THE NEWS AND KNEW HIS REIGN OVER THE FREEDOM OF SPEECH WAS OVER.

"Don't ever be afraid to speak out for what is right in your heart, in your mind, and for our country! All tyranny needs to gain a foothold is for people of good conscience to remain silent."

TJ RETURNED TO MONTICELLO, KNOWING THAT WHAT HE DID WOULD HAVE AN EVERLASTING IMPACT. BUT HE KNEW THERE WAS STILL WORK TO BE DONE AGAINST THE EVIL KING. HE POLISHED HIS PEN AS HE WAITED FOR THE NEXT CRISIS, AND FOR EVIL TO REAR ITS UGLY HEAD. *AFTER ALL,* TRUTH JOTTER THOUGHT, *THE PEN IS MIGHTIER THAN THE SWORD.*

About the Authors

BRANDI AND KYLE MCELHANEY ARE NATIVE MISSISSIPPIANS WHO BOTH GRADUATED FROM OLE MISS. KYLE IS A CAPTAIN IN THE US ARMY AND THEY ARE BOTH INDEPENDENT DISTRIBUTORS OF HEALTH AND WELLNESS PRODUCTS. THEY HAVE TWO BOYS THAT ADORE SUPERHEROES. KYLE HAS A LOVE FOR EARLY AMERICAN HISTORY AND BRANDI HAS A PASSION FOR WHIMSY. WITH ALL THEIR POWERS COMBINED, THE *FOUNDERS FORCE* SERIES WAS CREATED. THEIR GOAL IS TO STRENGTHEN THE AMERICAN FAMILY AND CREATE A NEW GENERATION OF PATRIOTS.

About the Illustrator

Michael Nozinich is an illustrator and graphic designer living in Los Angeles, California. He is originally from Memphis, Tennessee and graduated with a Bachelor of Fine Arts from the University of Mississippi. Michael is passionate about art as well as being an avid sports fan, gamer, and all-around nerd.

Have a book idea?

Contact us at:

Mascot Books

560 Herndon Parkway

Suite 120

Herndon, VA

info@mascotbooks.com | www.mascotbooks.com